RAPPAMAN

MUST BE

RED

ALL OVER

BY DONAVAN CHRISTOPHER

Rappaman Must Be Red All Over
Copyright © 2016 Donavan Christopher

Published by Caboodle Books Ltd 2016.

A Catalogue record for this book is available
from the British Library.
ISBN: 978-0-9933000-7-3
Page Layout by Highlight Type Bureau Ltd, Bradford
Printed and bound by CPI Group (UK) Ltd, Croydon, CRO 4YY

The paper and board used in this book are natural recyclable
products made from wood grown in sustainable forests. The
manufacturing processes conform to the environmental regulations
of the country of origin.

Caboodle Books Ltd.
Riversdale, 8 Rivock Avenue,
Steeton, BD20 6SA, UK.

Dedications to:

Lisa, Leevan and Sheri:

To all of you who have shown a joy and love for my Raps and poems, I hope this collection of thoughtful poems that must be read can be a guide towards your future positive actions, and also comfort in times of sorrow.

To those who may be just joining us, we welcome you with open arms, and hope you also will enjoy this book of Rap and poetry. In the words of our philosophy R.A.P!

RESPECT ALL PEOPLE

Spread in near and far as a thick loveable layer, so that it should stick forever and ever. If you possess not the desire to win and spread Risspek, even though the battle may seem lost, then you're probably not the best one for my team.

Thank you to the team at Caboodle for all their support and to my favourite artist Mr Chris White. And not forgetting my mentor along this wonderful journey, Mr Nick Toczek, who has always been there with great words of support and advice whenever I was in doubt about any particular shout. Also Christina Gabbitas of The Children's Reading Festival of which I'm an Ambassador. And not least Liz Lemal for all her skills and support decoding and presenting this collection of my latest works.

Nuff Risspek and keep the flame alive if Respect is to truly survive. Until we all meet again, remember we're really all very much the same.

CONTENTS

1. A BOUNCING BABY

Another

Bonny baby bouncing blubbery,
Always adorably apparently,
Beautiful, blissful, bawling **boldly**,
Yip, yapping, yawning yippee.

Burp, belch,
Always, alert.
Biological, beauty,
Younger yesterday.

Beaming bright,
Assured alright,
Brilliant, blushing, bouquet,
Yo yo yodelling,

Allowed!

2. ALL THE SAME

Wouldn't it be mad and so insane, if we all looked
and lived the same?
There'd be no one to curse and no one to blame,
No pointing fingers at people again.
All of us would have all the fame,
And when we performed nobody came.

We played and lost, all the same.
We walked and talked, all the same.
With smiles and faces, all the same.
We cried and bawled, all the same.
Kissed and chased, all the same.
Opened our mouths, all the same.
And fed our kids, all the same.
And put on our clothes, all the same.
And painted our toes, all the same.
Our eyes and nose, all the same.
We sleep and breathe, all the same.
And filled with grief, all the same.
Our hair and teeth, all the same.
Fingers an' arms, all the same.
Feet and legs, all the same.
And even heads, all the same.

Wouldn't it be mad and so insane?

Still let me go on, all the same.
Like apple and pears, all the same.
A drip, a leak, all the same.
And water and wet, all the same.
Fish and squid, all the same.
Steak and beef, all the same.
Goat and sheep, all the same.
And remember, don't forget!
I said,
All the same.

I could go on, but all the same,
From the wondering that seems to scour my brain.
But I'll stop right now, all the same.

And say thanks and Risspek!

All the same!

3. ANALYSE

Life is a discipline if you understand yourself,
It's not all about money, riches and wealth.

Before money I'd rather have good health.
This gives me strength to earn some wealth,
To gain more knowledge, under my felt,
And a chance to get to know myself.

Get to know yourself
B4 yourself gets to know you,
And you start to make excuses for yourself.

Get to know yourself
B4 somebody gets to know you,
And you start to make excuses for someone else.
We are but for a time, but life and words are forever.
Remember winners never skip,
They do what's right to achieve their glory,
So don't annoy me with a flossed-up story.

Don't spit into the wind,
Into the wind some spit verbal diarrhoea.
Every negative deed, intent, spent,
Sent to their face, their spit draws near.
In time themselves they begin to hear.
So listen to yourself
B4 somebody listens to you.

You shouldn't make excuses for yourself,
Except analyse correctly the things you do.
And if you analyse honestly, with good intent,
Then all your deeds will be blessed and true.

4. B.C.G.A. AWARDS

Bolton's Children's Graduation Awards
{Passport to success}

Bolton's pupils' achievement awards two thousand
and fifteens,
Presenting young achievers from primary to their teens.

B.C.G.A. you know it's our name,
For now and the next generations
Education is the name of our game,
And the reason for these presentations.

Schools and parents thought there was a need
For an organisation to support them and their children's
needs.
A report was soon swiftly produced,
So their children's education would not be misused.

It's B.C.G.A., a passport to success,
Everyone's a winner, but it's up to you to do the rest.
If you put in, you generally take more out,
If you don't put nowt in, then yu don't take nowt out.

It's a vision of achievement, attainment, fulfilment,
To work in partnerships with families and parents,
Educational establishments and other organisations,
To raise their expectations and aspirations.

Bolton's pupils' achievement awards two thousand
and fifteens,
Presenting young achievers from primary to their teens.

Giving them lots of adulations and standing ovations,
With congratulations and family celebrations,
So families and schools build better relations,
And global citizens for the next generations.

And it's simply the reason,
For these great presentations.

5. BE INVOLVED

Please read a book to be involved,
And a lot of your problems will be solved.
They make your troubles melt away,
And give you hope for a brighter day.

It's time to go deep in a heap of knowledge,
By the time you finish you're ready for college.
A book is not only words on paper,
You can store it in your mind just like data.
By reading books you can read new words,
They'll be in your head like wise proverbs.
Books take you to another dimension,
Don't be afraid to show your intention.
Reading can improve your creativity,
And can also be your best activity.

A book is touchable, precious knowledge,
One book today and tomorrow it's college.

6. BETTER EQUIPT
(ConneXions)

Beware! It's like a jungle out there.
Beware! You better take care.
Beware! Of idle procrastination.
Beware! You need salvation.
Beware! Go get some re-education.
Beware! Or better get to ConneXions.

Beware! It's like a jungle out there.
Beware! You better take care.

Are you aware! Of opportunities there?
Are you aware! It's not Goldilocks and the bears?
Are you aware! It's the now gen service?
Are you aware! It's the Y.P.S.?

Offering personal development and social education,
Advice and support to youths of all sorts.
To choose the right course, weather, commerce or sports,
Help set targets, levels and goals to score,
Still it's a journey of choice where you explore.

ConneXions the teenage years,
Professional support to dispel your fears,
Giving you style and credibility with extra gears,
As you take a step into your new careers.

Find uz in schools, colleges and access places.
Don't loaf out your days,
Walking through all types of mazes.

For advice and information,
There are other conceptions,
But it's up to you
To make ConneXions.

Note: Y.P.S. = Young People's Services

7. BETWEEN THE MILES

Can you taste what I taste?

Or even face what I have to face?

Then could you live the way I live, and could you give up
what I have to give?

Would you say what I have to say?

Or could you be you every minute of the day?

Do you see what I see, or do you guess at what I see?

Can you really speak for me to judge my fruit by its tree?

If you assume to presume the way I feel,

It will only make it worse for the truth to reveal.

I understand and hear your empathy,

But it still doesn't always make it right for me.

Should tomorrow come I'll still be me,

To prove all over again it's the best I can be.

8. BONNY AS A BUTTON

Bonny as a button when T'naya arrived,
Bonny as a button, a family full of pride.
Bonny as a button, her eyes, nose, and chin,
Bonny as a button when she begins to grin.
Bonny as a button when she begins to smile,
Bonny as a button, just let her sleep a while.

Bonny as a button when she's drinking down her milk,
Bonny as a button, her skin is smooth as silk.
Bonny as a button when she has to burp,
Bonny as a button when she's sick on Granddad's shirt.

Bonny as a button when she has a bath,
Bonny as a button when we hear her laugh.
Bonny as a button when she sleeps in my arm,
Bonny as a button she makes the world seem calm.
Bonny as a button when she's being fed,
Bonny as a button when Mum and Dad put her to bed.

Live-acated to my first Grandchild

(Note: Live-acated, a word used for Dedicated }

16

9. CHOICES

A choice is a decision, a decision is a choice,
It can be almost silent or even a noise,
A wink, a nod, a gesture or a voice.

Don't be led around like donkeys or cattle,
Some decisions can be your biggest battle.

A decision is an option, a surmise of the mind,
It's the result of the issues of things you decide.
To take a chance, a short cut, so you can try and glide,
Every decision is a journey, but don't joyride.

You will have to make decisions for yourself,
But it's wise to take counsel if you need a little help.
A council with the wise, a council of your peers,
Then balance up the odds and dispel away your fears.

Decisions, decisions will have to be made,
Just be true to yourself, no need to be brave.

10. CRIME RATE

We be taking down crime to a minimum rate,
Let's do it today, today's the date.
Zero 800 three 5s three 1s.
The number to call to cash in your bonds.

Yo it's me and my crime stoppaz,
Check it check it, wi not the coppaz.
Am stopping crime wid my crime shoppaz,
Because nowadays it seems like nobody bothaz.

Some will some won't, some just can't cope,
Some live in fear without any hope.
Some cry some die, some live to lie,
While some just laugh and tek it fi joke.
Thought you saw me, nar you don't,
When I appear and disappear there ain't no smoke.

Invisible peeps, it's time to speak,
Let's clean up avenues, lanes and streets.
Where kids love to play and families love to meet,
The pot's boiling over so let's turn down the heat.

I'm the general ambassador for crime stoppaz,
I never have to speak to the coppaz.
Representing, crime preventing,
Life extending and community mending.

It's not about revenge yo not even payback time,
Am being true to me, am being true to my mind.
You never see what we do, we're always fighting crime,
No need to drop a nickel, I'm on a free line.

So only you can set yourself free,
To be FEARLESS.ORG just like me.
Zero 800 treble 5 treble 1,
The number to call if you want crime _ _ _ _!

11. DALTON SCHOOL J.I.N.

England West Yorkshire Huddersfield Dalton for sure,
To lands far away our junior school so pure.
A school that's truly blessed from above,
Filled with multicultural love.
More happy faces than track shoe tears,
I speak for the children of Class 14 clear.
To work with you has been a pleasure,
The hospitality I cannot measure.
Like a stranger in the night you took me in,
I hope the knowledge I left was edifying.
I write this to you all az I go,
For to write it later my heart would be low.

We all must part and go our ways,
But I am sure we'll remember rap poetry days.

I could go on but now I must end,
And I hope someday
We'll meet again.

Dedicated to the children and staff at Dalton School J.I.N.

12. DESIRE

They, who desire,

Piece of the world for themselves,

Do not truly desire for peace.

Is not all over everywhere, mine and yours to simply share?

If a picture can paint a thousand wordz,

Then tell me,

Why does a poet want to write?

Has he nothing better to do with his time

Than turn darkness of matter into beams of light?

And why do some youngsters desire alcohol

When they cannot hold the liquor?

They're only trying to act big I think,

And trying to rot out their liver.

I quiver.

Why such a desire to grow to be old?

To be nearer to your gravest soul?

Or just nearer to being so cold?

The fact of the matter is the matter of the truth,

Desire the days of your life especially your youth.

13. DISTRACTED JOURNEY

Who disturbed my liberty, my serenity, my journey?
From this nightmare I must awaken.

The big ships they all came fully laden,
And left with many African maidens,
Thrice laden.
Man, woman, child,
I was also taken.

Away from my wife, my life,
My land, my sky, my rivers, my sun,
My ways, my drum,
And delivered into the hands of my oppressor.
From the hands of traitors, some I had thought as
brothers,
To be bound up like a mad dog,
A captive into servitude and forced labour a slave.

Nigger!

And Boy was my name,
To them that held me tight in their chains.
From unconsciousness I regained,
From their beatings once again.
MY MIND
STILLS FEELS
THE PAIN.

I SHALL
BE FREE
AGAIN.

14. DRIFTING

It's always nice to find a place where you can drift away,

A space in time where it all stands still,

No static traffic or super highways.

A place where you can hear your heart beat,

And thoughts of bliss pleasant and sweet.

Just a place where you can drift away,

If not Tomorrow then why not Today.

15. FOOD FOR THOUGHT

Don't be afraid of the school's high gate,
Walk with pride and don't be late.
Stick together like birds of a feather,
Help out a friend in many, any weather.

Here's a message and food for thought,
Always remember what you've been taught.
So stick to your rights, it should not fail,
As sure as a fact you will prevail.

A few years from now you'll need a job,
I hope and pray you shouldn't have to rob.
Education is a cert, so don't get too distracted,
"I don't want to hear you've been subtracted.

So don't be afraid of the school's high gate,
You are the new student the academy awaits.
You'll make new friends from a different place,
Remember your knowledge and tools of grace.

Make life your reality and not a dream,
You're all now students of our team.
And if anyone should ever treat you mean,
We can be there to clean up the scene.

So here's a message and food for thought,
Always remember what you've been taught.

16. HOW TO LIVE

How to live in the 6 (21) 20 21 18 5,
Get all your odd jobs done now,
So you won't have to do them later.

Don't let odd jobs pile up in your attic!
This will only make you panic.
Always know the nature of Risspek,
Adhere to be honest and you'll impress.

Stay on top of your education,
Or you'll spend time going back to school,
Unless you already intend to.

If you can invent a time machine,
This will save you bags of time.

Change your attitude to improve,
Look after your health, why not start today?

As the 6 (21) 20 21 18 5 is already on its way.

17. I AM

I am forever judged, misunderstood,
I am not dead wood for the frozen cold,
I am not to be sold.

I am a book, you see my cover,
But I know within page to page,
Chapter to chapter, verse to verse,
Yet still you rage and curse,
Make things worse for yourselves.

Your shelves remain empty,
But cannot forget me,
Store me or stop me.
You assume me, try abuse me,
Accuse me, try confuse me,
Even though I am precise, wise and concise.

You emotionally kill me,
Educationally starve me,
Economically deprive me.
I am the book you tried to destroy, would not employ,
Even tried to tear out my pages, at life's key stages,
In your krazy mad rages.
But I am

The book, pages like mercury,

Infinite my pages are the air you breathe.

You would truly wish I don't succeed,

And between your lines I must see and read your deed.

But I am the sound before the tock!

Or the space between the ticks of a clock.

I am

The lick, from the flick of my wrist,

And truly without me,

You simply wouldn't exist.

18. IF I WERE A CLOUD

Imagine if I were a cloud,
What would I be like?
Fluffy, grumpy, angry or bright?
Would I be huge, small, tiny or large?
Would I cruise, drift or float like a barge?
Would I be friendly with the sun or would we argue
and shout?
And would I be missed when I'm not about?
Where would I sleep? I can't stay out at night,
As when night falls I'm not so bright.
I know when I'm upset my tears roll down,
To make things green that were recently brown.

This is something that makes me very proud,
Wouldn't you spend a day as a cloud?

Try shutting your eyes just like me,
As when they're shut I still can see.
Gently swaggering along with the breeze,
As a cloud taking life at ease...

Imagine.

19. I'VE SEEN

I've seen so many things I shouldn't have seen,
And can't erase them from my mind.
Been so many vivid places and walked with all mankind,
But my destination I still cannot find.
I've been many a places I shouldn't have really been,
And seen faceless places I shouldn't have even seen.
I have said things I shouldn't have said,
And it was probably wiser to keep them in my head.
I've also done things I shouldn't have done,
All in the gain of shame and having some fun.
And I've even won things that I shouldn't have won,
But I was determined to carry on my run.
Though the troops seemed defeated and the battle
looking lost,
And to the victor the spoils, bitter was their loss.

But in all of the things I've experienced and done,
I found knowledge, understanding and gained wisdom.

Note: All experiences are good and bad, but both will teach
you wisdom and will guide your approach within
your future actions.

20. KNOWLEDGE

If I prick you with a pin you must say **ow**!
So get some **knowledge** and then go wow!
When you **KNOW** you'lL have the **Edge**,
Like a wise old **Owl** you'll never fall foul,
And be left on a lonely **ledge**.

Say when, where, what, who, how?
Investigate thoroughly, start right **now**.
There can be many pitfalls wherever you go,
A simple word of wisdom can be just to say **no**.

You'll never be fooled or be **led**,
As the key to your education lies within your head.

Note: there are **8 key words** to be found in the word knowledge,
9 if you include the word knowledge.
The words are not to be rearranged to make a word like wedge.
Find and use the 9 words to make your own poem about Education and Knowledge.
Make suitable rhyming couplets for each word,
Then create rhyming sentences for your poem.

21. KNOWLEDGE AND POWER

Knowledge is power so I've heard them say,
If such are the facts I'll need some today.

Information I'll devour every minute every hour,
Each tiny book I'll scour in search of ill power.

But is power strength or electricity?
As the best place for knowledge is the university.

Note: ill Power = Great / Fantastic

22. LET UZ FLOW

Let us flow yo

Let us flow yo

If you wanna give poetry a flow yo

Like a solo

Or a duo,

Grab a pen and paper an' let's start today.

The **P** in POETRY it stands for Peace,

Spread it in the North, South, West and East.

The **O** is for Oral to spread the good news,

And even an option to change your views.

E is for Educate and Eradicate hate,

T is for TRY to do your best,

R has got to be RESPECT,

And **Y!**

Because it's just what you should simply reflect.

23. MATHEMATICAL PIE

* Means answers open to discussion, and how many maths formulas can u find?

Add flour, add marge,

An egg an' water too.

Multiply all that you need to make a few?*

Sprinkle carrots, potatoes, coriander, calaloo,

A few chunks of lamb

For the pie or the stew.

Roll out the pastry for the greasy tins,

Tidy as you flow, throw your rubbish in the bins.

That's what you've got to really do,

To feed how many people?

Seven, three or two? *

Now neatly trim the excess from round the radius,

Or let it just remain; just use it as a crust.

Subtract from the cupboard

Knives, forks and plates.

With crockery an' cutleries you need to equate,

How many tables, how many chairs,

So all your group can sit and eat in a square?*

Each table to have its own equal share
Of hungry fresh faces all sitting there.

What mathematical formulas will you actually need
For this task to shape and truly succeed?*

It's your answer, make a decision,
But mind the reaction from your pen's precision.

Now you're ready to serve up a hot meal,
If your answers were true and if they're all real.

For all the hungry faces sitting patiently there,
They should all have deal of an equal share.

So how many pies did you eventually make
To serve up swiftly on each plate?

Note: I'm sure there's a puzzle in this or try creating your
own pie puzzle.

24. ME AND MI TV

Am TV sitting watching TV,
Am TV sitting me and mi TV,
Am TV sitting by mi TV,
Am TV sitting watching electricity.

The BBC can be contraire,
Unless they show a good documentary,
Whether it's BBC2 or Free view,
Channel Four, Five an' ITV.

Am a cushion louch and love mi couch,
All mod cons with remote pouch.

Turning up the volume, change the channel aghen,
I never miss mi news, especially News at Ten.
Me and mi TV wi like best of frenz,
She looks at me and I watch her aghen.

Am TV sitting watching TV,
Am TV sitting me and mi TV,
Am TV sitting by mi TV,
Am TV sitting watching electricity.

When our eyes meet its love that I see,
Her eyelids a flicker, a flickering at me,
I punch all her buttons, she's my TV.

Contrast a picture full of colour and brightness,
Oh my TV as regal as my highness.

If I fall asleep I know she really cares,
Because over every snore, she stands there and stares.
Or winking, blinking,
I'm thinking just for me!

Then I wonder why I dream about mi TV.

25. MI BACK A BUN MI

Woey mi back a bun mi

Woey mi back a bun mi

Woey!

Mi back bena bun mi di udder day.

Mi feel like mi did cripple,

Mi nuh young again an sipple.

Dem seh is a trap nerve, well it definitely get pon mi nerve.

Sciatica,

A it mek mi nah walk proper,

It still a bun likkle yah now,

But mi a go true.

Mi get fi realise it good fi do exercise.

But woey!

Mi back a bun mi, mi back a bun mi,

Woey!

Mi lay down flat and guess what?

Woey!

Mi back a bun mi, woey mi back a bun mi,

Woey!

So mi go pon mi side and yes yu guess.

Woey mi back a bun mi, mi back a bun mi,

Note: Woey = Woe. Bun Mi = Hurting. Bena = Been. Udder = Other.
Sipple = Supple. Nuh/Nah = Not. Yah =Here

26. MIRACLES

I don't want to sound cynical,
But why can't this be a miracle?
When you sleep and wake the following day,
And you're able to walk, talk and play,
A miracle happens every day.
As we know not the hour or time,
It's the same for all mankind,
A miracle happens every second, no needs to think
or even reckon.
When we fly so high above the clouds,
Alone above, below the crowds.
The earth she is mighty, vast and proud,
When through air we soar, how's this allowed?
A miracle happens every minute,
So I wrote this down in a lyric.
Something gave us all of this, to make our lives full of bliss,
It's a miracle I insist, and know it's something
we all will miss.
The earth is so beautiful from above,
Please show your neighbour lots of love.
As when you see the earth from the air,
This is the reason we all should care.
Where would we live if we didn't live there?
Miracles happen every day.

27. MISJUDGED

Miss, who is Misjudged and where does she live?
What is her purpose, she seems privileged?

She seems to have her say all of the time,
Is not this life I live supposed to be mine?

Who is Misunderstood and where does she come from?
Is she also a judge that sings the same song, same song?
Like I always thought Misunderstood,
As when I know I over stood.
Then she said she was always Misheard,
Which confused me even more.

Then I asked Misinterpret to explain.
She said it was Misrepresentation of the word Miss,
Which was always being Misused.
She said Misrepresentation Misheard Misunderstood.

Misheard was confused and so was Misused,
She said do I still need an explanation?
I said no, Miss,
And sorry I ever gave it so much attention.

28. MORNING WORLD

Morning Moscow, morning world,

I wanna give a shout to all you boys and girlz.

I wanna say yo, I wanna say bless,

It all simply means nuff risspek.

So there you have it, am here as a guest,

And the moral for the day is just do your best,

It's the only way to obtain success.

I'm an alien, a visitor from outa space,

I'm just like you but with different ways.

Anything you've got I've got too,

And I might have a like bit more than you.

And oh it's true everybody's got a view,

The things I do, you might not do,

And the things you do I might not do.

I'm Donavan Christopher from England, Yorkshire,

But mi muma and mi puppa were born in Jamaica.

So I've got a likkle bit a style yah, mix up in a Patois,

So now we just call it a like bit of Yardsha.

R to the A to the P.P.A.,

Everyone does things in a different way.

29. MY SCHOOL RAPPORT

This is my school Rapport,
To remember some of the things I've been taught,
And some of the things I've had to abort.

My school Rapport must be red,
So a world of minds can be fed.

Donavan's ambitious, thoughtful and kind,
This Rapport is strictly from my mind.

Friends I've won and foes I've fought,
If making trouble was swiftly caught.
Was always in my teacher's thought,
When I passed a test expecting nought.

First year high school now year seven,
Just arrived looking smart and just turned eleven.
Group of lads buckling down
To see who could be the biggest clown.

Timetable, map and compass jus to navi round,
You'd find me in the head's room or even lost and found.
Dinner times were always meek,
Yorkshire Tates, sprouts, fish or meat,
If you got up or someone nicked yu seat.

Those days were cool and really sunny,
When Leon pulled out a deck wi lost our money.
So a lesson today I've also learned,
Don't play cards, you'll get your fingers burned.

This is my school Rapport,
To remember some of the things I've been taught,
And some of the things I've had to abort.

Now lessons came thick and fast,
Some watched the clock from to, to past,
How long was this lesson going to last?

It was really easier to show interest,
Other than giving your head the usual rest.
So slowly started to show my best,
Never wanted to settle for anything less,
And applied myself to pass each test.

Science was acid and alkaline,
Sulphur gases and prism time.
Mixing solutions, litmus paper,
Watch the colours changing like magic later.
Bunsen burner, test tube flex,
We all would scatter when Mr Hmmm got vex.

This is part of my school Rapport,
To remember some of the things I've been taught.
And some of the things I've had to abort,
So I wouldn't end up in a jester's court.

30. MY TRAVELS

I love going out, out and about,
Boy do I love travel.

I travel by car, bus, TAXI! and train,
And if I'm really lucky I travel on a plane.
Travel's good for yu blud and circulation,
Seeing lots of words that are hard to mention.
People going out in different dimension,
Hand gestures made for an explanation.

Seeing how people relax and live,
Some are poor, some are exclusive.
But it broadens the mind to think positive,
The further I travel the more I live.
I love going out, out and about,
Boy do I love travel.
My name is pounds, shekels, dollars or plastic,
I'm like literal, currency an' automatic.
If you don't have me then you have to step it,
But it's nice to have me in your purse or wallet,
Because I'll never be your worse meal ticket.
I love going out, out and about,
Boy do I love travel.

31. MY YESTERDAYS

A flash back to my yesterdays,

They're also called my childhood days.

When thunder stormed, wear your wellies,

A Milky Way was two old pennies.

Chocolate wafers were a snack and for 10 old pennies a

Caramac,

Chocolate machines outside every shop, 10d a bottle for

Ben Shaw's pop.

Power cuts, miners' strikes,

Houses glowed, from candle lights.

And to cross every busy road,

We were taught the Green Cross Code.

Bright arm bands to reflect car lights,

Schooldays were sometime dark as nights.

Carol singing and sunny smiles, for bob a job you'd walk a

mile.

Doing stuff getting smart, join the cubs and play your part.

At Boys Brigade subs were paid and marching feet when

brass bands played.

Back lane stream catching trout, never a time we lounged

about.

Japs and commandoes down to outings,

One team hides the others start scouting.

Round camp fires roasting spuds we almost lived our lives in
the woods.
Climbing trees for apples and conkers,
Then playing cricket and bowling Yonkers.
Pinching strawberries happily from an allotment,
To pinch a few strawberries was very important.
Playing footie was our main leisure,
Me and my mates would play forever.
A hand-sewn ball made of leather that simply got heavier in
rainy weather,
I look back now, it just made us better.
Swing ball, bench ball, gate ball, slam,
If you won a game of slam, you knew you were the man.
Three and in, cuppies, a small sided match,
5 minutes in goal, to save or catch.
Borrow your mate's ball if they couldn't come out to play,
We'd bring it back later or the very next day.
Lorry cart races from the top of the hill,
To win a cart race you had to drive with skill.

We had to be home and in by eight,
And if your watch was slow you couldn't be late,
Or face the inquisition of a leather debate.

You'd never be allowed back through the gate,
But all my yesterdays were truly GREAT!

32. NEW BRAND SMILE

School's got a face lift, a new brand smile,
The builders didn't work swift,
We've had to wait a while.

To all of the pupils the future looks bright,
We're looking brand new like a rainbow light.
2, 3, 4 more classrooms to write,
Now we've got space when it used to be tight.
Our double glazing is so well amazing,
Now we're all gazing instead of lazing,
Gazing at recourses to help all our causes.
Like I.T. suite, new nice unique,
Be proud, have pride, it all belongs to us.
Or would you rather have it back,
Just all as it wuz?
So let's work together, for better as a team,
Make sure our brighter future was not just a dream.

There's still something we should not forget,
To everyday yo show nuff Respect,
R.A.P.P.
Respect all people's property.

33. NOT EVERYBODY

You can pick it out from the air,
Love is there for all to share,
But not everybody possess love.

Some will glare at your nightmare,
Some for you simply just don't care,
Some will laugh at your expense,
Some make sure the die is cast,
Not everybody possess love.

And some would rather see you die,
While some would prefer to see you cry,
And some would wish you didn't exist,
But within their ignorance they want to persist,
Not everybody possess love.

With pen to paper clenched in grip,
Let me give them all a tip.
Infinite infinity like an abyss,
They all should know,
Love is this.

34. PEEL an IDEA

Peel back an idea right to the core,
And inside there you'll find more storage,
For more ideas for you to haulage,
Dive inside and even explore-idge.

Peel back your ideas, explore your thoughts,
I mean at the end of the day you don't want to
End up with noughts!

Ideas can pass you by every each day,
When I get an Idea, I lock them away.
Embezzled in paper for a year an' later,
Being refined, loved and polished, because later they're
greater,
And will be cherished.
Or as it was simply written, they shall be simply said.
Some forged in thought, squints and expressions,
To bring a tear, a smile or a lift from depression.

I peeled back a thought today of mine,
And another poem just leapt from my mind.

35. PIE COOKERY CLASS
{Easy as maths}

8oz of flour,
4oz of marge,
Mix it all together with a fingertip massage.

One free-range egg,
Now add it to the bowl,
Slowly pour the water,
Make sure that it's cold.

Now knead it all together, roll it nice and thin,
Don't use the iron please, use the rolling pin.

Next step to prepare the tin,
A smudge of butter, smudged within.
Place the pastry properly inside the tin base,
Any excess pastry will make the pie face.

Add berries, cherries and strawberry shapes,
Apples and pears sliced up with grapes.
Gracious, goodness the pie must have a face,
From the excess pastry that mustn't go to waste!
40 minutes set at gas mark 8,
To get your pie sweet and thoroughly oven baked.
Remove it, cool it, let it sit and wait.

Your pie should smell hmmm!
Your pie should smell great,
Fresh from the oven, freshly oven baked,
So pass me a napkin and hand me a plate.

With this pie,
You know I've got a date.
Then teacher said be cool, relax and we should just wait.

To take it home after Skool,
And give our folks a taste.

36. POEMS

Poems, poems, poems to rite,
Best time to pen a poem
Can be very late at night.

Thought it, heard it, under moonlight,
Not sure wen this poem will come alive.

Poems come from everywhere,
In every space, time and goggle-eyed glare.

To write a gud poem
You've 2 free your mind,
And research some facts that U can find.

A poem that's written is incubated,

WHILE A POEM THAT'S RECITED IS LIBERATED.

37. PUDDING AND CREAM

Gorgy Porgy pudding and cream,
Kissed the girlz and made them scream!
So the girls they chased him off,
They caught him and threw him
In a horse's trough.

38. R.A.P.P.

Rhythmic African peace poet

I'm a rhythmic African peace poet,
If you've read the book then you will know it,
Just the way I love to flow it.

Over the page with words I sow it,
Between the lines you get to know it.
Like a brush to paper I will stroke it,
Like an iron to the fire my pen will poke it.

Hearts and minds I begin to melt it,
As deep down inside I know you felt it.

And when it's real I know you feel it,
So now's the time to sign and seal it.

Just for you I will now reveal it,
My poems emit peace and now you know it.
A RHyTHmiC African Peace Poet.

39. RECESS

It's a time for reflection,
To Reassess and make the corrections,
During the reflections of your miss intensions,
You may have had during the day.
Recess
From the mess in your directions,
It's always blessed to make your own inspections.
Must be critical, no loose ends,
No need to be cynical, just clean your lens.
Every corner and creases,
No stone left unturned.
And if you're honest with yourself,
Then you will have learned.
Recess, reassess and then take a reset,
On yu marks, steady and just get set,
Then you're on your way to simply being the best.

Recess
Every day we should all try clean up our acts,
To stop, think, listen and break down the facts.
The past controls the future and even right now,
But if you don't stop and think you'll never know how.

40. RESPONSIBILITY

When responsibility comes knocking,
Try telling it you're not playing out,
Or even in.

RESPONSIBILITY

When responsibility calls,
Be prepared and of good cheer,
Don't be scared.
It's called Representation for the next generation.

GREAT RESPONSIBILITY

Now we're talking In Charge, Top Dog, The Don Dadda, A1,
Borse, Mi General, The Governor, Mother, Father, Jah Jah,
Your Majesty, the King, and Leadership!
Can you lead the ship through the storm?
Can you lead the sheep to pasture?
Great responsibility is to avert a disaster,
And bring in the Caviar, Bread or the Corn.

41. RIDDIM AND THE RHYME

With a **Riddim** and a rhyme,
And a rhyme and a Riddim,
You can truly free your mind.

And with a rhyme and a Riddim,
A Riddim and a rhyme,
There's always a **Word** for you to find.

Like rap, rhyme, **reason**, in any season,
With expression and cohesion
To pass away the time.

The art of illusion to calm the confusion,
A very good solution is to add a little fusion
To a Riddim and a rhyme,
And a rhyme and a Riddim,
Then with a rhyme and a Riddim,
And a **Riddim** and a **Rap.**

You can **RISSPEK All PEOPLE,**
Just like **dat!**

42. RISSPEK CAN MEAN

Respect can mean so many things,
Some think diamonds, pearls or bling blings.
Respect can mean so many things,
Like keep it clean and empty the bins.

Respect can mean we live differently,
But never to offend intentionally.

It's not about restraint or tolerance,
But what we can gain from our difference.
Respect can mean so many things,
Share, Respect and grow some wings.

What does Respect mean to you?
Should we fight over a view?
Shouldn't we just learn, from something new
From a courtesy stand and point of view?

We might have to fight to gain Respect,
But I'm always in fear of what might be left.

So let's stop getting so complexed,

And making people feel perplexed.

Like a darker place than the bowels of Hades,

Or the belly of Dystopia,

Within the walls echo's of screams and barbaric hysteria.

No escape they say,

Unless attitudes are honourably changed today.

Let us prevent a worldwide wilderness,

Alas! Then who will clean up after our mess?

Is it because we never agreed?

We had to burn our nest.

Respect can mean many things,

It should never mean distress.

WITH REAL RISSPEK!

EVERYBODY

WINS.

No voodoo dolls or poison pins.

43. RISSPEK IZ

Risspek iz our main subject,
We give respect, that's what we expect.
Please and thank you we never reject,
And never treat people like an insect.

Lyrical rhymez we're here to inspect,
If it not right or if it's correct.
Don't you worry we'll find the object,
All you got to do is remember Risspek!
It's Rappaman Rappaman here I am,
I build rhymez slow or fast as I can.
Rappaman Rappaman in your vicinity,
Everyone knows me as Donavan CEE!

Risspek iz our main subject,
We give respect, that's what we expect.
Please and thank you we never reject,
And never treat people like an insect.

Clayton B aka Peppery and Donavan C

44. SAVE THE PLANET

Let's start right now, we have to **Plan it,**
Today's the day we're saving the **planet.**
As everything in life you should really **plan it,**
I mean where would be without a **planet?**

45. STOP AND REFLECT

Surmise,
Don't let your thoughts go down the drain,
You know some people will put us all to shame.
Some don't hear so they lip read and sign,
They make a bad situation just seem fine.

And we choose not to even hear,
When our ears are totally fine and clear.
The blind learn to see within their world,
Would you give your sight to a boy or a girl
To see this beautiful glorious world?

Some people don't walk so they learn a new skill,
And you say you're bored with time to kill.
You only need to be willing and you'll be able
To take charge of your life and make it stable.

46. SUMTINGZ COOKING

Sumtingz cooking in the kitchen,
I wonder what the head cook is cooking.

Mash potato, roast potato, chicken an' dumpling,
I tell you what, it's got the lot.
It sweet like sumting,
I feel like jumping, jumping and jumping.

Sumting sweet to eat today,
Can't wait to grab my fork and tray.
Can't even wait for the rest of the day,
It's only first break an' we're out to play.

Hooray, hooray, play timez done,
I can't wait for lunch to feed my tum.
Hurray, hurray, I feel like a king,
When the next bell ringz, you will hear me sing.

Sumtingz cooking in the kitchen,
I wonder what the head cook is mixing.
Roast beef, roast lamb, curry wid stuff in,
Or owt you like, wid Yorkshire pudding.

Fish and chips on a dish are finger licking,
Treacle sponge gets fingers sticking.
Mustard for custard on your pudding,
With mates like mine who take the micking!

Sumtingz cooking in the kitchen,
I wonder what head cook is cooking.
If that's the bell then it's time to tuck in,
So grab your plate and let's all get stuck in.

Sumtingz cooking in the kitchen.

47. SUPER HEROES AND SHEROES
{Creating ways for the public to help the police solve serious crime.}

Albuquerque New Mexico 1976,
The history of Crimestoppers it begins.
Lend me your ears, you're listening pins,
Am telling you about their origins.

A young man working at a filling station,
To feed his family his main intention.
Shot and killed in his work situation,
Murder and robbery was the investigation.

The crime was done by local people,
Who never gave a thought for such evil.
Somebody must have some stored information,
Nobody called or came to the police station.

Albuquerque New Mexico 1976,
The history of Crimestoppers it begins.
Lend me your ears, you're listening pins,
Am telling you about their origins.
An idea was born for a new hotline,
For people to anonymously free their mind.
Local businesses financed the dream,
Broadcast by TVs so it could be seen.

The hotline number was a major success,
Translations received and the murderer's arrest.
There were also other crimes not reported before,
So yahll don't have to speak to the police no more.

www.fearless.org is the youth version of Crimestoppers.
Designed by the youths for the youths.

48. THE FIRST STORY

{7 six-word autobiographies inspired by anthology at Appleton Academy, Bradford}

The pen that stirred the world

I came I saw I wrote

Me, the man from another planet

I come in peace and love

Journey on a pen to Lalibela,

It's the rhythmic African Peace Poet

Rappaman said it must be red

49. THE FIRST STORY Pt 2

{7 six-word stories inspired by anthology at Appleton Academy, Bradford}

Write a poem free your mind

Write a poem watch it breathe

Write a poem give words life

Study Panic Sleep Wake Revise Pass

One more poem before I sleep

I live life to spread Risspek

Risspek is a six letter word!

50. THE SHOUTS Pt 1

The main thing is to get your idea down on paper
Before it disappears into a vapour.
If you can't remember it, how can you use it later?
Write it down, respect all pens and paper.

QUOTE DC!
Get your facts into your raps,
And your imagination into your fiction.

MAGIC REALLY DOES EXIST
How to make some magic,
All you have to do is make some time.
When we make time great and many things can
BE ACHIEVED.
We all have the power to make
TIME.

DYSTOPIA
When the silent get silenced transparency becomes a blur,
And justice can disappear.
When the silent are silenced
A dictator is on the rise.

51. THE SHOUTS Pt 2

IGNORANCE

Ignorance of mind will keep you blind,
You have to decide for yourself which words are best for
your health.
If what you do works for you, then all I can say is continue.

GUIDANCE

Remember there's always a guiding light to be found at the
end of any tunnel,
Also a guiding light as you go through one.

SWIMMING FOR LIFE

Life can be like swimming out into the open sea,
Not knowing where your next meal is coming from,
Or whether you're the next meal deal.

Note: Learn to catch fish!

52. THE SHOUTS Pt 3

CAN'T

If you look at the first three letters it says
CAN,
Which means 3 to 1 says you CAN.
The 'T is just for someone Tutting!
At you.

LETTERS

Letters develop words that we use, to help defuse
a few issues.
With voices and thoughts laid down in ink,
And letters and words to make people think.

WEAKNESS

That which is weak we endeavour to strengthen,
And that which is strong we endeavour to balance with
compassion.

STEPS

Sometimes we step back only to take a next direction which
helps us to continue on our journey. Every step has a
purpose and cause for us to fulfil.
So long as your goals are still in sight.

53. THE SHOUTS Pt 4

A QUEST
I wish you all the very best and remind you that you can be all you want to be, but you must make the first step and dedicate yourselves to your quests.

SPLASH TO RIPPLES
Remember even the smallest pebble thrown into the
middle of a pond
Makes a splash of disturbance to cause large ripples
in the water.
They come back and touch the shores
either vigorously or calmly.
But one must first throw the stone however small
into the pond.
We're not ready to throw boulders but will if needed.

POSITIVITY
Always look for the positives out of any experience,
good or bad.
In all experiences there is wisdom to be found.

SKILLZ

Your Skillz will always come into play once we start to
manoeuvre; we sponge up until we get that time to squeeze
out the bitters from the juice.
It always a part of you and once it starts it like going
auto pilot.

54. THE SHOUTS Pt 5

CREATIVITY

In a world of creativity

Time never seems to stop.

Only for a tad after the completion of a masterpiece.

With just enough time to step back and admire,

Before the mayhem starts all over again.

TILTED

I know the Earth sits on an axis,

But I see the word literal and straight,

And full of mystery.

OPPORTUNITIES

I love problems and fear them not,

I see them as an opportunity for another solution

to a new challenge.

4 THREE-WORD SHOUTS

Must Be Guilty

GUILTY OR NOT?

Speculation Or Inferences?

Where's The Evidence?

55. TOUR DA VALE
{Yorkshire}

A Yorkshire crowd can be loud and rowdy,

And always proud even when it's cloudy.

With streams of people lining streets,

All out an' about for Yorkshire treats.

Up road t'ova hill, darn valley an' through tu pass,

Aye binah, they'll be going like a blast.

Like clappers, crank and chain,

All wheels wheeling through tu vale.

Every biker covered in lycra,

TV cam on bike and man.

Darn in history it's all recorded,

So each, every rider can be lauded.

Aye, then back tu race what a spectacle,

It's the longest race on a bicycle.

Tha can't enter on a tricycle,

Tha be frozen out like an icicle.

Still the roads were filled with Yorkshire pride

To cheer each biker on their ride.

Yorkshire tea, pudding, steak, water and ale,

Were actually the best things at the Tour Da Vale.

56. U THOUGHT

Presume not the situation,

Assume not the intention,

Thought not the occasion,

There's nothing wrong at all with thinking these things

for oneself.

But when it's thought for support of someone else,

It's better to just ask for the facts,

It's really just as simple as that,

There should be no need to download the App.

A thought can be as good as a surprise,

It's what has made us foolish or wise.

57. WALKING BUS

Off to school kidz r uz,
Oh this morning, oh what a fuss.
Suzie, Paul and Rufus,
We're off to school on the walking bus.

Left, right, left, right, left, right, left.
Can you hear me, don't play deaf.
Left, right, left, right, watch us flow,
Left, right, left, right, steady as we go.

The feet on the bus go
Left, right, left,
Left, right, left,
Left, right, left.
The feet on the bus go
Left, right, left,
All the way to my school.

Off to school kidz r uz,
Oh this morning, oh what a fuss.
Suzie, Paul and Rufus,
We're off to school on the walking bus.

Through wind, rain, snow and stormy weather,

Kidz r uz we're all together.

Wellington boots, hats and coats,

Protect us all from getting soaked.

Scarves, balaclavas, mittens and gloves,

We don't need these when the sun shines above.

Doing our bit for the environment,

Walking to school on the pavement.

The feet on the bus go

Left, right, left,

Left, right, left,

Left, right, left.

The feet on the bus go

Left, right, left,

All the way to my school.

58. WORD OF ART

This is urban art and literacy,
Writing about the things I feel
And the things I see.
It also allows me to write free
And part of the cause to help me be.

Today's the day we're rolling smart,
Turning words into art,
And even tearing them apart.

This is graffiti on a page,
It's a world of life for you to engage,
It's an energetic force.
This is my poem ever staying on course.
My art is a world of light,
An art designed to bring you life,
Its purpose is first to be free,
To achieve as much or even more than me.
This is my art it's full of power,
That gets brighter by the second, and each hour.
This is the art that has to be fed,
And also your poem which has to be read.
This is my art which shall never fade,
This is my art and from the earth it is made.

My craft shall surely live for all with endeavour,
Bringing people and cultures living together.
Thinking smart and thinking clever,
Binding ties that should never sever.

And should it be ever torn apart,
I suggest you reading it again from the start.
To bind these words upon your heart,
Make it a factual living word of art.

RISSPEK!

59. XPLain

Will someone explain how the game's being played,
Then everyone will know exactly what they can do,
And what they expect,
And what they can't do to be correct.

I mean haven't you seen
This for that, that for this,
He got, she got,
Signed and sealed by that lot.

I just don't understand,
That this should happen in our beloved land.
Clemency, leniency,
A derogatory mockery of democracy,
With no proof or transparency.
I thought equal rights and true justice stood for all,
But it seems to have taken a
MIGHTY
Fall.
The future could be trouble,
For us all.

PUZZLES

1   How do you change a pound to a penny without spending, changing or giving it away?

2   What is the 6 (21) 20 21 18 5?

Thanks again for being so kind,

Please keep these thoughts in your mind.

Share risspek to keep it alive if common courtesy

is to survive.

Answer to pound to a penny, puzzle, Just switch 4 letters enny or ound.

Answer to what is the 6 (21) 20 21 18 5 = Future